Written by
Jackie Demeri Costello, LVCYT

Illustrated by
Michele Beckhardt-Lada

Recommended for All Ages

Text copyright © 2015 by Jackie Demeri Costello
Illustrations copyright © 2015 by Michele Beckhardt-Lada
Cover and interior design by Michele Beckhardt-Lada

Summary: A how-to book of yoga and activities to nurture creativity while learning fun animal facts.
Printed in the United States of America.
1 2 3 4 5 6 7 8 9 10
ISBN 978-0-9961518-0-1

The content of this book is for general instruction only. Each person's physical, emotional, and spiritual condition is unique. The instruction in this book is for educational purposes only and not intended to replace or interrupt the reader's relationship with a physician or other professional. It is generally advised that a medical professional be consulted before embarking on any exercise program. Please consult your doctor for matters pertaining to your specific health and exercise plans. The author and publisher disclaim any liability arising directly or indirectly from the use of this book.

Dedication

To my sons, Paul Angelo and Christopher, with all my love always.

Writing this book has made me ever more aware of all the people and animals I have known throughout my life to whom I owe a debt of gratitude. Special thanks to Joshua Rosenthal, Lindsey Smith, and the Launch Your Dream Book team at IIN; you truly make dreams come true! For so generously giving of their time, wisdom, and giftedness, huge thanks to: my wonderful teacher, Lakshmi Voelker; the inspirational Victoria Moran and Danielle Legg; the incomparable Lila Weisberger; radiant Shakta Kaur Khalsa; and the lovely Christi Eley. Eternal love and gratitude to my beloved father, Angelo Demeri; my grandparents, Trude and Walter Altschul and Antoinette and Carmine Demeri; and my mentor and teacher, Maryann E. Ferreri. Each one of you encouraged me to write and all of you live on in my heart. Hugs and much love to my mom Doris, my sister, Kathy and to Chelsea, Toni, Elyssa, Mindy, and Lorene for cheering this project on and for their brilliant editorial suggestions. Much appreciation to Tracey Kocz for her enthusiasm and invaluable editorial work. Love and gratitude to Gene for patiently reading and rereading this manuscript, answering countless questions, and smiling the whole time. Thank you from the bottom of my heart to my cousin Michele for the precious illustrations and a lifetime of friendship. Countless thanks to all my students; you have also been my teachers. Though space precludes me from mentioning all the cherished teachers, family members, and friends who have given me so much, you know who you are and, along with my love and gratitude, I extend to you a heartfelt Namaste.

Biography

Jackie Demeri Costello has over 25 years of experience teaching children, families, adults, and seniors. Her work is inspired by a love for people and animals, along with a passion for making yoga and creativity accessible to all in a fun and empowering way. A certified Lakshmi Voelker Chair Yoga Teacher, Jackie has completed additional Yoga Alliance accredited teacher training programs, including KRI's 200-hour level certification with Hari Kaur Khalsa. She also holds a Diploma with Distinction in early childhood education from the London Montessori Centre. Jackie graduated Magna Cum Laude from St. John's University, is certified in holistic coaching from the Institute for Integrative Nutrition, and is accredited by the American Association of Drugless Practitioners. She has studied extensively with Lila Weisberger, founder of the International Academy for Poetry Therapy in New York City and is currently enrolled in Victoria Moran's Main Street Vegan Academy.

Jackie continues to learn about animals from her little dogs and farmyard friends at Lewis Oliver Farm on Long Island. She would love to hear about your Animooves experiences and can be reached at Animooves@gmail.com.

Michele Beckhardt-Lada is a Graphic Designer, Illustrator, and Owner of Beckhardt-Lada Design, a graphic design studio creating original illustrations for products. Michele graduated from Parsons School of Design, NY, with a BFA in Communication Design, and studied advanced graphic design at School of Visual Arts, NY and Mercy College, NY. Michele resides in Westchester, NY with her husband David, two sons Brian and Cameron, and rabbit Maxine.

See more of Michele's work at facebook.com/beckhardtladadesign, cafepress.com/beckhardtladadesign, as well as on Twitter, Instagram, and Vine. She is reachable at beckhardtladadesign@aol.com.

To Sophia and Kyle
enjoy with Grammie

Michele Beckhardt-Lada

CONTENTS

INTRODUCTION

Welcome to Animooves! Animooves was created out of a love for animals and yoga-style movement. Yoga was originally inspired by many of the natural ways animals move and stretch. When people copied these movements, they found it helped improve their health and well-being. Movement is so important for us, but often we spend long hours seated on chairs. Just like a plugged-in iron that automatically turns off when it is left to sit for too long, our body systems start to shut down when we sit still for extended periods of time. Animooves is designed to help keep our systems active even while we are seated. Animooves provides techniques to help balance the body, mind, and emotions. We also expand the fun to include creative writing, games, animal facts, and activities to help us learn more about farm animals and ourselves. You might be surprised at how much we have in common! So, come along and bring your family and friends. Animooves is great for all ages!

Chapter 1

POSTURE POINTS

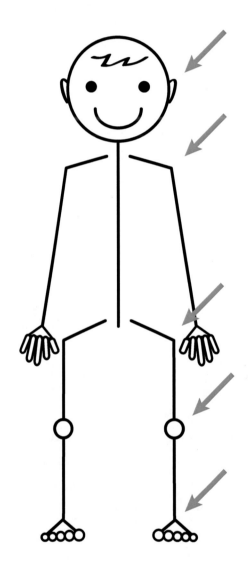

Animooves begins with good posture. Good posture is based on proper alignment, whether we are standing or sitting.

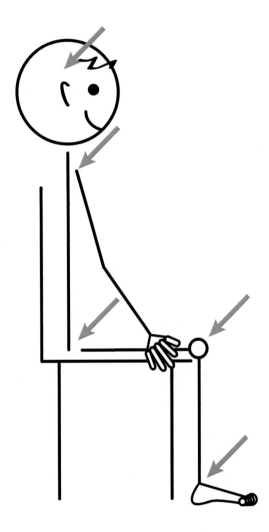

How can you tell if your body is properly aligned, especially if you aren't in front of a mirror? That's where Animooves' four *posture points* come in. They make it easy to be sure your body is in good form by lining it up from bottom to top.

Posture – Stand or sit with your legs and feet about hip width apart. Let's start with a focus on our feet; they form the foundation. Wiggle your toes, and let them relax and spread out. Notice if you are putting most of your weight on one area of each foot. Balance it out by bringing three main areas of the feet in contact with the floor – the pads below your big toes, little toes, and your heels. Lift up your arches.

Now that we have created a solid foundation, we are ready for our first posture point.

1 Knees Over Ankles

Make sure your knees are directly over your ankles. This will help protect your knees. If your knees tend to move in toward each other or out and away from each other (this tends to happen more often when we are seated), shift them so they stay over your feet. Now, press your feet firmly on the ground. Notice how that lifts your upper body.

2 Hips Level

Place your hands on your hip bones, adjusting your posture so that your hips are level. If you are sitting, balance your weight evenly on your seat muscles. Pull in your belly button very, very slowly. You will feel the lower part of your spine, also known as the tailbone, gently move downward, lengthening the spine. Great! Now you are ready for the next posture point.

3 Shoulders Over Hips

Roll your shoulders up toward your ears and then back and down. As you bring your shoulders back, try to gently squeeze your shoulder blades together. Then, relax your shoulders down. Check to be sure your shoulders are in line with your hips: directly above them, not leaning forward or behind them. Create l-e-n-g-t-h in your spine, and give all your precious organs in your midsection lots of space by lifting your rib cage up (not out) and away from your hips. Good job!

4 Ears Over Shoulders

Place one hand behind your head and one behind your neck. Very gently press your head and neck into your hands. Be sure to keep your chin lowered and level. Do not arch your head back. When your ears are over your shoulders, relax your hands down by your sides.

Whether you are seated or standing, you can line up your body posture this way any time you feel yourself slouching.

Activity: Grow an Inch!

Players: two or more. *Items needed:* measuring tape, chair (optional), paper, pencil.

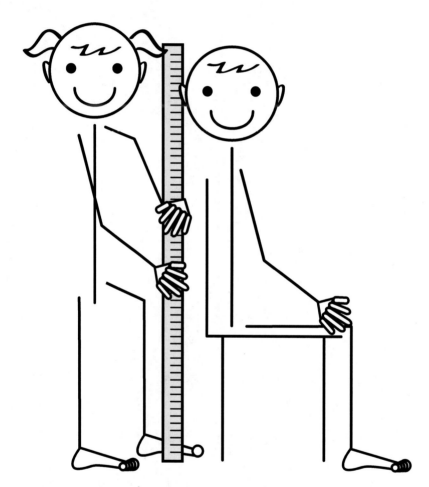

1   Stand or sit without using your Animooves posture points.

2   Have another player measure your height and make a note of how tall you are.

3   Align your body using your Animooves posture points.

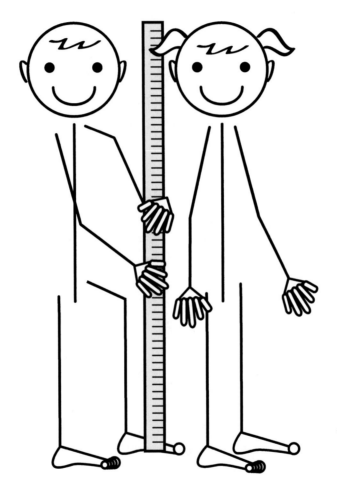

4   Have the other player measure you again. Make a note of the measurement and compare it to the first one. Usually, aligning your body will increase your height by about one inch.

5   Take turns so that everyone has a chance to grow an inch!

6   *Smile!*

Facial Posture – Now, let's bring our attention to our faces. Did you know that your face has a posture, too? Most of us tend to make the same facial expressions over and over, until they become habits. Have you ever noticed that people who are worried or thinking hard about something tend to move their eyebrows toward each other, making lines form between them?

Our facial muscles reveal a lot about our mental and emotional states, but did you know that the way we hold our facial muscles can also affect our mental and emotional states? For example, if we clench our jaws, a message is sent to the brain that we are under stress. This sets in motion a chain reaction in which the brain releases stress signals to the body.

If we were truly in some type of danger, we would need the body to go into a ready-for-action state known as *fight-or-flight*, so we could fend off an attack or run away. To help us do this, the body shuts digestion down and circulates blood to our arms and legs so they can move faster. Once we are finished running away or fighting, our body calms down again. However, if we are not in actual danger, but simply clenching our jaws out of habit or thinking of something that makes us feel tense, these bodily stress responses are not necessary. Instead of helping us, they can actually have a negative effect, interfering with our body's ability to digest our food, absorb nutrients, and rest.

The good news is that by becoming aware of the way we hold our facial posture, we can reverse this process. We can relax our facial muscles. Here are three Animooves posture points for your face to help you do this.

1   Squeeze all the muscles in your face very tightly, hold for a few seconds, and then completely relax them.

2   Relax your jaw and let your lips part softly. If your eyes are closed, let your eyelids be very smooth, not squinting shut. Relax your forehead and scalp. The more you practice, the easier it will become. Soon, you will be able to recognize when you are holding tension in your face so that you can release it.

3   *Smile!* A smile sets in motion healing and inner happiness. Smiling is good for you and those around you.

Smiling – What if there were a sheep among those around you? Would smiling matter? The answer is yes! Researchers have found that sheep share many characteristics with us regarding faces. They remember faces. They feel safer, more comfortable, and happier around familiar faces, even if it is a photograph of another sheep or person they know. When they see other sheep, they prefer to be around those with calm faces, rather than those who look upset. When sheep see humans, they prefer people who smile at them.[1]

Smiling is good for our body and mind. One of the best ways to help us smile more is to think of things that we are thankful for. It can be something big or small. Some people keep a gratitude journal to record things that they are thankful for each day. Studies have shown[2] that people who keep gratitude journals become happier. You might want to keep a gratitude journal, too. The following *Animooves Writes* can help you get started:

[1] Amy Hatkoff, *The Inner World of Farm Animals: Their Amazing Social, Emotional, and Intellectual Capacities* (New York: Stewart, Tabori & Chang, 2009), 127–30.

[2] Emiliana R. Simon-Thomas, PhD, "A 'Thnx' a Day Keeps the Doctor Away," *The Greater Good: The Science of a Meaningful Life,* December 19, 2012, accessed February 2015, http://greatergood.berkeley.edu/article/item/a_thnx_a_day_keeps_the_doctor_away.

Animooves Writes: Counting Smiling Sheep

List five things you are thankful for:

1

2

3

4

5

Done already? List five more:

1

2

3

4

5

Chapter 2

A BREATH
OF FRESH AIR

Every human being and every farm animal must breathe in order to live. A breath of fresh air can mean just that; it is a time when we inhale the fresh, green scent of spring or the crisp, autumn smells of leaves and pine needles. The phrase "a breath of fresh air" can also mean something that brings new energy and refreshment to a place or activity. Animooves incorporates both of these meanings. We breathe in deeply, which brings precious, fresh oxygen to our cells. We exhale completely, releasing and relaxing our body. While we breathe, we pay attention to what we are doing. We breathe in different ways to create different results. In this way, we can energize ourselves when we are feeling tired or relax our mind and body when our thoughts are racing.

Our breath is so powerful that it can help us move our body, our thoughts, and our emotions. Just like our facial expressions both reflect and influence our emotions, so does the way we breathe. To understand this better, without using words, try to act out the following feelings, just by the way you breathe:

Frightened   Angry   Relieved

When we are upset or nervous, we usually breathe in a very shallow way, where only the upper chest moves. For many of us, this shallow type of breathing becomes a habit. As a result, our bodies react as if we're upset and our minds follow, even when we aren't really in a stressful situation. When you acted out emotion number 3, relieved, did you let out a long, full exhalation or a "sigh of relief"? When we breathe in deeply and exhale completely, our body and mind get the signal that everything is OK, and we become calm.

Have you ever watched a peaceful baby breathe? When babies breathe in, their stomachs expand; when they breathe out, their stomachs draw in. If you look closely, you might notice that babies breathe in and out through the nose, not the mouth. The nose works as a filter to clean, warm, and moisten the air before it enters our bodies. It might take a little practice to get the hang of breathing this way again, but it is worth the effort. When we do, our minds become clear and calm, we have more energy, and our bodies digest food and absorb nutrients better. Here is how it is done:

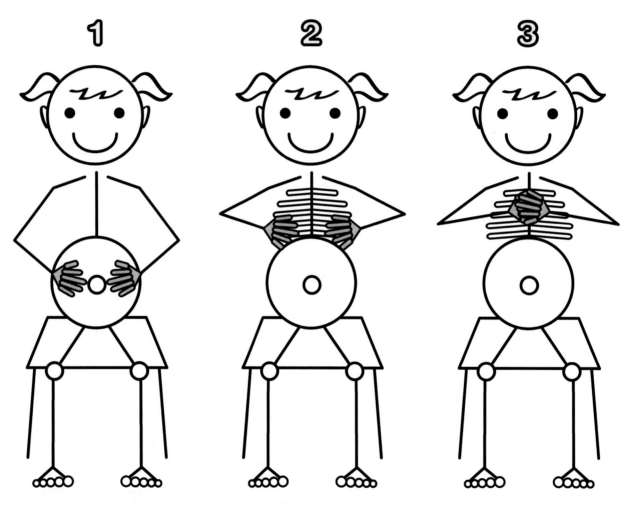

1   Place your hands on your belly. Relax your stomach muscles. Inhale through your nose, and let your belly expand with the breath, like a balloon filling with air. Exhale through your nose and draw your belly in toward your spine.

2 Slide your hands to your ribs, with fingertips facing inward, toward each other. Inhale deeply through your nose, letting your belly push out again and your ribs expand out to the sides; your fingertips will move away from each other. Exhale through your nose, drawing the belly and ribs in, fingertips moving toward each other again.

3 Next, move your hands so they are crossed over the center of your chest. Once again, as you inhale through your nose, let your breath expand your belly and then your ribs out to the sides. Lastly, let your chest rise. Exhale through your nose, first releasing the chest down and then moving the ribs in toward each other. Finally, bring your belly toward your spine.

Great! You did it! This is the way we breathe most of the time when we practice Animooves. Try breathing this way when you are lying down with a small pillow or toy on your stomach; notice how it rises and falls with each inhalation and exhalation. You can also think of a word or phrase along with the breath to send a nice message to yourself. Thich Nhat Hanh, a meditation teacher who was nominated for the Nobel Peace Prize, often suggests thinking, "Breathing in, I calm body and mind. Breathing out, I smile." [3]

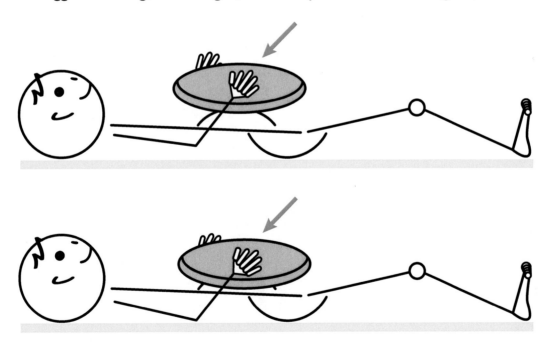

[3] Thich Nhat Hanh and Arnold Kotler, *Being Peace* (Berkeley, CA: Parallax Press, 1987), 15.

Animooves' Moo Breath will help cool your body down after you exercise. This technique also works really well to help calm anxiety.

Animooves' Moo Breath:

1   Inhale deeply through your nose.

2   Exhale through your mouth in this special way: say the word, "Moo." Notice how your lips move into a rounded shape to do this, as if you were holding a straw in your mouth. Exhale, blowing out the air as if you were blowing into a straw. Make the exhale nice and long.

3   Repeat several times until you feel calm and relaxed.

Activity: Try these activities that put the power of the breath into motion!
Items needed: straws, cotton balls, paints, paper

1 Blow through a straw to move a cotton ball.

2 Inhale through the straw to hold the cotton ball on the end of the straw.

3 Dab a blob of paint on paper. You could use one color or several different colors. Blow gently through the straw to move the paint and create new designs.

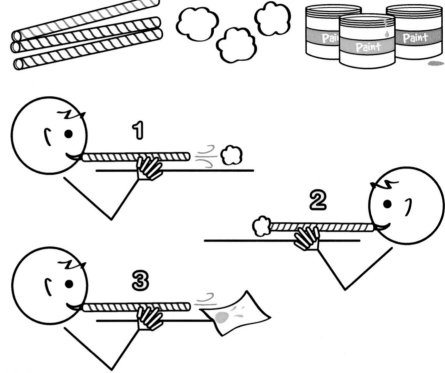

Animooves Writes:

Write your own Breathing Messages to use when you practice your breathing techniques.

Breathing in, I _____

Breathing out, I _____

Breathing in, I _____

Breathing out, I _____

Chapter 3

CONNECT: BREATH AND MOVEMENT

How do Animooves help improve focus and memory and relieve stress? When we practice Animooves, we connect our breath with our movements. In this way, the breath becomes like a bridge between our body and mind. We think about what we are doing, and we become focused. In order to remember something, we have to have paid some attention to it first! We learn that we can bring this same kind of attention to other activities, too. When we pay attention to our breath and our movements, we are aware of the present moment; this helps clear our minds of other thoughts, and we become calm. **Let's try it!**

Usually, we inhale on opening and expanding movements and exhale on closing or folding movements.

Here are some Animooves warm-ups that connect breath and movement.
You can do them separately or before a full Animooves sequence. They are great to do when you are sitting on a chair, too, but be sure your chair is stable and sturdy.

Remember to do your warm-ups very slowly. Our bodies are different each day. If a certain movement doesn't feel right for you to do today, respect your body and skip it.

Always begin with your Animooves posture points to align your body.

We will warm up the body from head to toe. Remember to inhale and exhale through your nose when practicing these Animooves.

1 Keep your chin level and head centered while you inhale. Exhale as you slowly turn your head to your right. Inhale back to center. Exhale as you slowly turn your head to your left. Repeat several times, concluding the way you began, with your chin level and head centered.

2 Inhale as you lift both arms up over your head. Exhale as you release them down. Do these movements very slowly. Repeat several times.

3 Inhale as you extend your arms out to the sides. Exhale as you release your arms down. Repeat several times.

4 Inhale while you lift your right shoulder up toward your right ear. Exhale as you bring your shoulder back and down. Repeat three times. Do the same movement and breath pattern three times with your left shoulder. Then, bring both shoulders up together on an inhale and relax them back and down on the exhale three times.

5 Press your palms together with your elbows out to the sides. Inhale while you face forward. Exhale as you turn from your waist to your right. Inhale back to center. Exhale as you turn from your waist to your left. Inhale back to center. Repeat several times.

6 Place each thumb in the hinge where your hips and legs meet. Inhale. Exhale as you extend your spine and bend forward, hinging from your hips (where your thumbs are placed). Keep your chin lowered. By extending forward this way, you keep your spine lengthened as one complete unit, from tailbone all the way through the back of your neck. Next, draw your navel in toward your spine as you come back to an upright position.

7 Inhale as you lift and extend your right leg up. Flex your foot to lengthen the muscles behind your knee. Exhale and release your leg down. Do this three times. Repeat the same movement and breath pattern with your left leg three times.

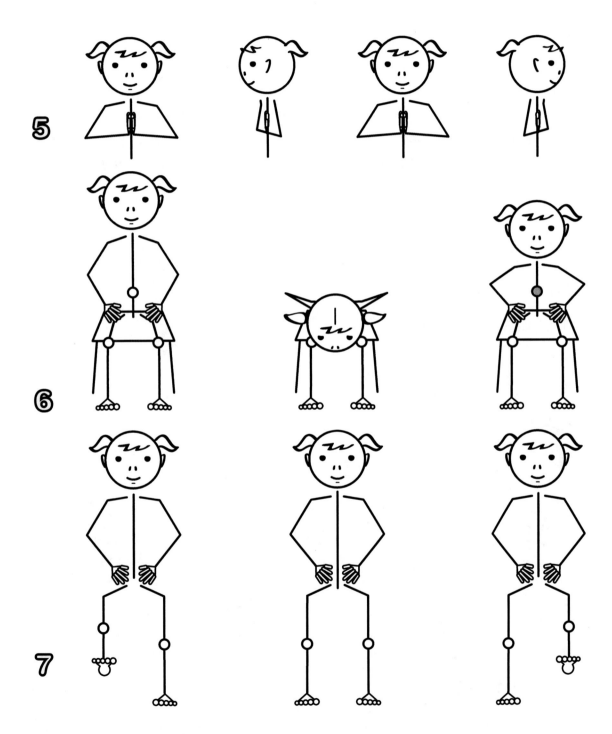

5

6

7

Were you able to stay focused on your breath and the movement? It gets easier with practice!

When we think about what we are doing, no matter what it may be, we tend to make fewer mistakes and remember more details about it. It seems the same is true for cows, too! Several studies have been done where buckets, some filled with food, were set up along the course of a maze. Cows in the study remembered where the buckets with food were, even after several weeks. Pretty a-*maze*-ing.[4]

Activity: Pick a spot in your home, perhaps the top of your night table or the kitchen counter.
Without going over to look at it, try to write a list or draw a picture from your memory of all the items that are there. Check to see how many you were able to remember.

[4] AT. Ksiksi* and E. A. Laca, "*Cattle Do Remember Locations of Preferred Food over Extended Periods*," Queensland Department of Primary Industries, Australia, *Asian-Aust. J. Anim. Sci*. 15, no. 6 (2002): 900–904.

Animooves Writes:

Think of a memory that makes you smile. An example might be a trip to the beach. Try to remember as many details about this memory as you can. Use words that describe how your five senses experienced it. The five senses are sight, hearing, taste, touch, and smell. To continue with our example of a day at the beach, you might choose to describe the color of the sky, the sound of the waves splashing, the sweet taste of watermelon you ate while you were there, the feeling of the sand between your toes, and the clean smell of the salty ocean air. Set a timer for five minutes. Write about your memory for the full five minutes. It's OK if you repeat yourself in your writing; just keep your pen or pencil moving and have fun. When the timer goes off, stop writing. Read what you wrote, and if you like, draw a picture of your memory.

Chapter 4

A DAY AT
THE FARM ANIMAL SANCTUARY:
ANIMOOVES FOR ACTIVE TIMES

A farm animal sanctuary provides a loving, caring, permanent home for farm animals. At a sanctuary, farm animals live balanced, healthy lives, with plenty of exercise so they stay strong and happy. A farm animal sanctuary often shares fascinating facts about the animals with the people who come to visit. There are farm animal sanctuaries in many communities. Perhaps there is one near you that you can visit.

Now, join us for "A Day at the Farm Animal Sanctuary: Animooves for Active Times."

Some of the goals of this sequence are to keep our bodies flexible, balance our brains, and energize and strengthen our bodies and minds.

We accomplish these goals by:

1   moving our spines in all directions – this helps keep our bodies flexible

2   doing movements where we cross the midline, or center, of our bodies – this helps balance our brain and improves coordination

3   activating our core muscles – this helps make our bodies stronger

4   releasing negative thoughts – this helps strengthen our minds

This sequence is done while seated. When choosing a chair, be sure it is strong, stable, and sturdy to support your movements safely. If you use a yoga mat, practice with bare feet to prevent slipping. You might want to keep some water to drink nearby. It is important to stay hydrated, but take small sips rather than big gulps. Also, it is best to do your Animooves on an empty stomach. Remember that your body is different each day. If a movement isn't right for you to do today, respect your body and skip that one. If you have any health conditions or concerns or take any type of medication, please check with your healthcare provider before doing any type of exercise. If a movement is challenging for you, just go slowly and keep practicing. Try not to criticize your performance; instead, applaud your efforts to do something good for your body. Be safe and gentle with yourself. Most of all, be sure to *smile* and have *fun*! Begin the sequence with your Animooves posture points, some deep breaths, and warm-ups. Remember to breathe in and out through your nose when practicing Animooves, except when performing the moo breath technique, when you will exhale through your mouth.

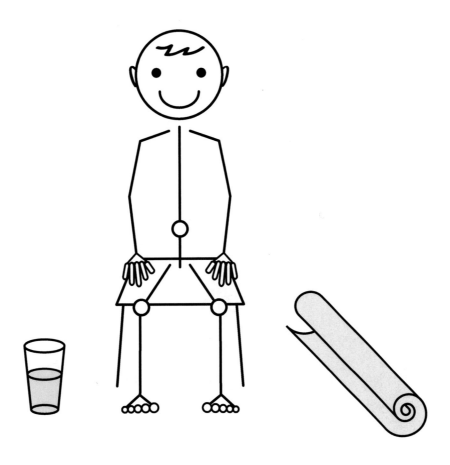

Cow Pose and Cow Counterpose –

Did you know that cows are very intelligent and feel happy when they solve a problem? Scientists measured changes in brain-wave patterns in cows with a test called an EEG (electroencephalogram). When the cows figured out a solution to a problem, their brain waves showed their excitement, their heart rates increased, and some jumped in the air! [5]

In cow pose and cow counterpose, we will flex the spine. The EEG test has also been used to measure changes in the brain waves of people who performed spinal flex exercises. The results of the test showed that people were calmer and more alert after three minutes of spinal flexing. [6]

Cow Pose:

1 Sit up tall. Place your hands on top of your thighs. If you are on a mat, you can have your legs crossed or extended out in front of you.

2 Keeping your chin level, inhale and gently arch your back, chest moving forward and shoulders moving back. Hold for several seconds.

3 Exhale back to your aligned posture.

Repeat several times slowly. If you like, you can increase the speed as your body warms up.

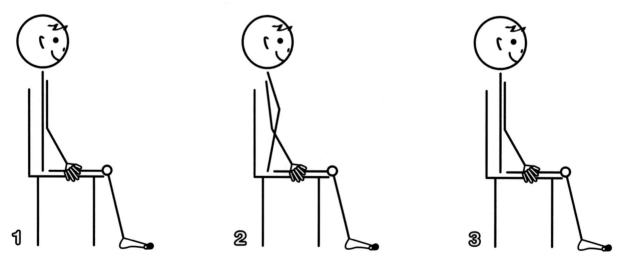

[5] "Farm Sanctuary," Farm Sanctuary, accessed January 2015, http://www.farmsanctuary.org/learn/someone-not-something/110-2/.

[6] Machelle M. Seibel and Hari Kaur Khalsa, *A Woman's Book of Yoga: Embracing Our Natural Life Cycles* (New York: Avery, 2002), 43.

Cow Counterpose:

We balance our body by moving in opposite ways.

1 We will begin this pose in the same position as we did for cow pose, with our hands on top of our thighs. Inhale.

2 Exhale, this time drawing the navel in toward the spine and rounding your back. Hold for several seconds without straining.

3 Inhale back up to the starting position.

Repeat several times slowly. Increase your speed, if you like, as your body warms up.

Rest for a few moments. We rest between all our Animooves. When we rest, our bodies absorb all the benefits of our movements.

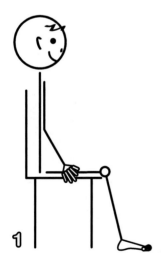 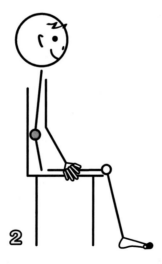 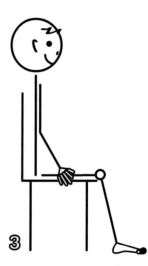

Goose Victory Twist –
Geese travel in a V-formation, taking turns leading, resting, and honking to encourage each other to keep up. In this cooperative way, they achieve their goals and get where they want to go!

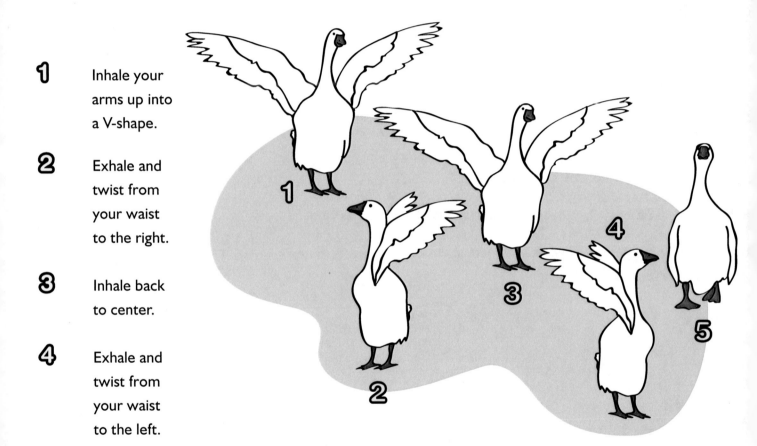

1 Inhale your arms up into a V-shape.

2 Exhale and twist from your waist to the right.

3 Inhale back to center.

4 Exhale and twist from your waist to the left.

5 Finish by inhaling back to center, and then exhale as you relax your arms down, resting your hands in your lap or at your sides.

Repeat the movements several times, and then rest for a few moments.

Smiling Side Stretch –

When rabbits feel very happy, they jump and twist in the air in a movement called "the binky dance." When we do this side stretch, we curve our body into a half-moon shape that looks like a sideways smile.

1. Begin in your aligned posture. Hold on to the right side of your chair. Inhale your left arm up. Sit up very tall. Lift your ribs up and away from your hips.

2. Exhale as you gently stretch over to your right. Press into your feet and lengthen your fingers. Keep the sides of your body lengthened.

3. Inhale back up to starting position.

4. Exhale and release your left arm down very slowly. When your palm and shoulder are on a parallel line, turn your palm down as your arm relaxes down the rest of the way. This will help protect your shoulder. Repeat on the left side. Rest.

1   2   3   4

Chicken Wings –

Chicken Wings – At Lewis Oliver Farm, an animal sanctuary in Northport, New York, one of the hens flew up into the rafters of the barn and laid her eggs. The volunteers didn't know what had happened until they heard some unexpected peeps! Chickens are very loving mothers, gathering treats for their chicks and teaching them how to peck for food.

1 Bring your arms out in front of you, bent at the elbows, palms open and facing in toward you. Try to have your elbows touch. This will work your chest muscles.

2 Inhale as you move your arms away from each other, squeezing your shoulder blades together.

3 Exhale, bringing your arms together again into the starting position. Repeat several times. Move in a rhythmic way, like a chicken flapping its wings. Come back to your aligned posture. Relax your arms down. Rest for a few moments.

E-I-E-I-O – This mini-sequence works your core muscles. We use these muscles for just about every movement we make, so they are very important. They also protect our back. We strengthen our abdominal muscles by working them until they are tired and then resting. When a muscle has been worked until it is tired, we say it is "fatigued." If we continue to try to work our stomach muscles when they are fatigued, we tend to use our back instead, possibly causing a strain. Please pay attention to your body and rest when needed. There are several ways to do this sequence.

When we sing, we breathe. When you do this mini-sequence, sing the "E-I-E-I-O" refrain from the song, "Old MacDonald Had a Farm." You might feel a little silly doing that, but sometimes being silly is a good thing! Also, when it becomes too hard to do the movements while singing, it is a clear indicator that you need to rest.

Our movements will create E, I, and O shapes with our body to work our core muscles.

"E" **1** Draw in on your navel point to activate the abdominal muscles even more.

A If you are seated on a chair, you may keep your legs down or, for a greater challenge, extend them both out in front of you. You can also alternate extending one leg and then the other.

B If you are seated on a mat, you can extend your legs out in front of you and allow them to rest on the mat. For a greater challenge, you can alternate lifting one leg at a time and letting it hover parallel to the mat and then releasing down before you lift the other leg.

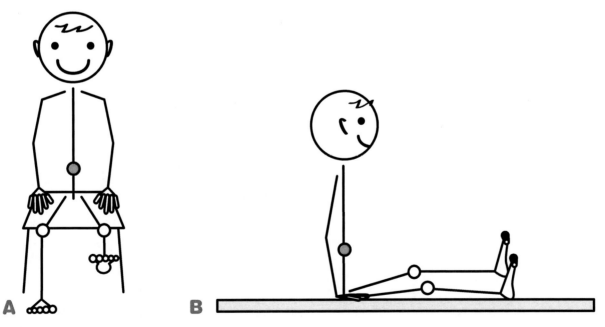

A   **B**

2   Extend your arms out in front of you, with your right arm raised higher than the left, so that your body forms the letter "E."

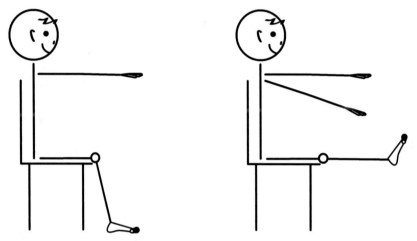

   1   Release your legs down and extend your arms up over your head, palms touching and thumbs crossed. This will be your "I."

2   Resume the "E" posture, this time with your left arm raised higher. Repeat the "I" posture.

"O" **1**   Extend both arms out in front of you, fingertips touching as if you were hugging a tree.

2   Alternate doing a half-twist to your right and then left. This will work the muscles on the sides of your abdomen.

Repeat this mini-sequence as many times as you like.

This is a vigorous series. When you are done, use your moo breath technique to cool your body down. Then rest for a few moments more.

When we make movements that cross the midline of the body, we stimulate both hemispheres of our brain. Since each side of the brain controls different functions, these movements may help improve our coordination, balance, and concentration.

Turkey Walk – In her fascinating book, *The Inner World of Farm Animals: Their Amazing Social, Emotional, and Intellectual Capacities*, Amy Hatkoff explains that turkeys "quickly learn to navigate the places they frequent daily. Given the opportunity, they can learn the details of a terrain of more than one thousand acres in the course of a year and keep that information in mind." [7]

Now that takes brains!

Let's take a walk across an imaginary terrain and balance our brain hemispheres along the way! You can do this pose seated in a chair or lying down on a yoga mat.

1   Inhale and raise your left leg; at the same time, reach across your midline with your right hand and touch your left leg (if you are lying down, try reaching toward your feet).

2   Exhale as you relax the arm and leg down.

3   Repeat the movement the opposite way; inhale your right leg up, and reach across your midline with your left hand to touch your right leg.

4   Keep "walking" this way, alternating sides. Try to work up to three minutes. For another type of challenge, try doing this with your eyes closed. When you are done with the turkey walk, use your moo breath technique again to help your body cool down. Rest for a few moments more.

[7] Amy Hatkoff, *The Inner World of Farm Animals: Their Amazing Social, Emotional, and Intellectual Capacities* (New York: Stewart, Tabori & Chang, 2009), 55.

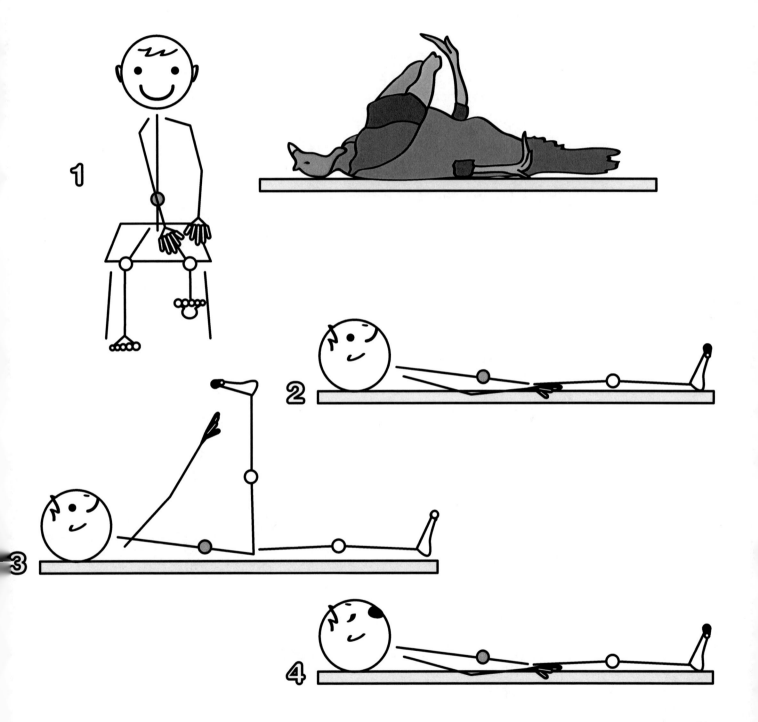

1

2

3

4

Feather Breath Technique – Let's complete our day at the farm animal sanctuary with a breathing technique that helps clear our minds of unwanted thoughts. When we release negative thoughts and feelings, we give our minds and bodies more energy to focus on things that make us happy. [8]

1 Sit in your aligned posture. Rest one hand in the other, palms facing up.

2 Imagine you are cupping a feather in your hands. Inhale deeply through your nose.

3 Exhale through your mouth as if you were blowing the feather away.

4 Next, think of a thought or feeling that you would like to release. Imagine you have placed it in your palm. Inhale deeply through your nose.

5 Exhale through your mouth and blow away the negative thought or feeling. Repeat this several times.

6 Now think of something that makes you smile.

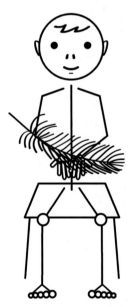

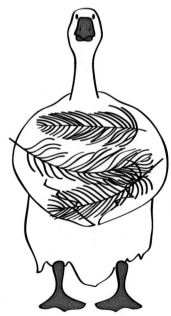

[8] Feather Breath Technique, adapted with permission from *Radiant Child Yoga Teacher Training Manual*, Shakta Khalsa, 2015, www.childrensyoga.com.

Activity: Brain-Body Challenge!

1   Interlace your fingers. Notice whether the thumb of your right or left hand is on top.

2   Separate your fingers and try interlacing them again so the thumb of the opposite hand is on top. For example, if your right thumb was on top the first time, rearrange your fingers so the left thumb is on top.

People tend to move in the same patterns so often that these patterns become habits. Yoga practice challenges us to become aware of these habits and experiment with new ways of moving. This helps keep our brain-body connection active. Challenge yourself to do some activities in new ways. Try brushing your hair with your brush in the opposite hand or pick up marbles from the floor with your toes. Some of these activities might seem difficult at first. Keep it fun and light. Simply observe what you are doing, congratulate yourself for trying, smile, and try again.

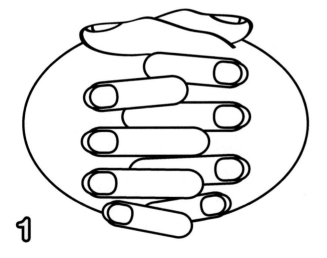

1

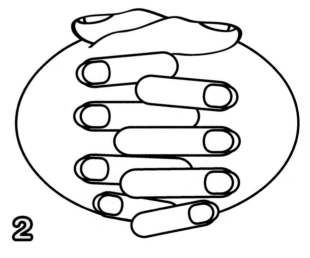

2

Animooves Writes:

Writing can help us understand ourselves and one another better.

Misunderstood: A Pig's Tale

Pigs are often thought of as dirty and sweaty. The truth is pigs are not sweaty. They don't even have sweat glands! They roll in the mud because that is how they keep themselves cool.

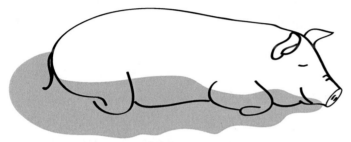

A Myth That's Hard to Swallow:
Goats' Eating Habits

Goats have a reputation for eating garbage, including tin cans. This is completely false! Goats are very particular about the quality, freshness, and cleanliness of their food. The intelligence and care they bring to what they ingest helps protect them from parasites and illnesses.

Have you ever been misunderstood or judged by others who were mistaken about something you did or said? How did you feel? Have you ever misunderstood or misjudged someone else? How do you think he or she felt? What would you like to say to the person who misunderstood you? What would you like to say to the person you misunderstood? What would you like the person you misunderstood to say to you? Does it make it easier to forgive others and ourselves when we realize that everyone makes mistakes? What does the word *compassion* mean to you? Can we have compassion for ourselves? What would you like to say to yourself?

Write answers to these questions in a notebook or journal.

Chapter 5

A NIGHT AT THE FARM ANIMAL SANCTUARY: ANIMOOVES FOR QUIET TIMES

All animals need rest. Rest and relaxation help renew our bodies and minds.

Sometimes our days are so busy that it is hard for us to relax and get a good rest. "Animooves for Quiet Times" is a sequence designed to help you release tension in your muscles and calm your thoughts.

This sequence can be done while seated in a chair or lying down on a yoga mat.
It is nice to do this sequence before bedtime, too.

Be sure you have a blanket or shawl near you, in case you need it to keep warm. As we relax and become still, our bodies tend to cool down.

If you can, dim the lights while doing this sequence.

1 Take several deep breaths in and out through your nose using your Animooves breathing technique.

2 You may close your eyes while doing the following steps.

3 Focus your attention on your feet. Consciously curl your toes in, and squeeze the muscles in your feet. Inhale and hold for a few seconds. Exhale and relax your feet, allowing the toes to spread out.

4 Flex your feet, activating your calf muscles. Draw up on the muscles above your kneecaps. Tense the muscles in both of your legs and your seat muscles. Take a deep breath and hold the tension for a few moments. Exhale and let your lower body completely relax.

5 Inhale. Exhale, bringing your belly button in toward your spine. Draw your ribs toward each other. Squeeze those muscles for a moment, and then release them.

6 Make fists with your hands, and flex your biceps. Bring your shoulders up toward your ears. Inhale, and hold. Exhale. Let your shoulders relax down and your arms and fingers hang loosely at your sides.

7 Squeeze all the muscles in your face in toward your nose. Hold for a few moments. Release the hold on the muscles in your face. Allow your jaw to relax with your lips parted slightly. Let your eyelids be smooth and closed gently.

8 Let your whole body completely relax.

9 Enjoy the peaceful feeling.

10 When you are ready, slowly begin to wiggle your fingers and toes. Rotate your wrists and ankles several times. Inhale, stretching your arms overhead while lengthening your legs and pointing your toes. Exhale as you relax your arms and legs down.

Farm Animal Sanctuary Relaxation Story:

Have someone read this story to you while you relax, or record yourself reading it aloud to listen to during a quiet time.

Heartbeats and Heart Bleats [9]

The night sky is an inky blue and scattered with stars. The air is filled with the sweet scent of hay and pine shavings. In their barns, the animals get ready to sleep.

The piglets snuggle in close to their mother. The other pigs cuddle up, snout to snout.

The sheep nestle into a cozy bed of straw. They brush against one another's faces, like a goodnight kiss, before they settle down to sleep.

The young goats play, bumping horns, until the older goats guide them to a warm corner of the barn where they settle down to rest.

The mother hen covers her chicks with her wings.

[9] A *bleat* is the sound a sheep or goat makes.

On the farm, all the animals become very quiet and still; only the gentle movement of their breath and the soft rhythm of each heart beating within them fills the silence.

Activity: Pulse Meditation

Sitting quietly, rest one hand in your lap. Find your radial pulse by placing the index and middle finger of your other hand very lightly on the inside of your wrist, below your thumb. Don't press too hard. Also, be sure not to use your thumb to find the pulse, because the thumb has a pulse of its own. Once you find it, try sitting very quietly, with your eyes closed, focusing your attention completely on the rhythm of your pulse. Relax.

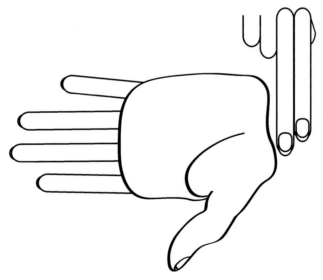

Animooves Writes: Write your own relaxation story. Have someone read it to you while you relax, or record yourself reading it aloud to listen to during a quiet time.

CONCLUSION

Even though you have reached the end of our book, we hope this is just the beginning of many fun hours of Animooves. To continue your Animooves adventures, please visit our website at www.animooves.com.

Miss Emily and Buttercup will be there to greet you and share more Animooves yoga, fun animal facts, and activities.

Buttercup is small but strong, like the flower of the same name. A buttercup flower's petals reflect light. Buttercup invites you to help bring light to animal awareness. Learn more about animals and share what you know.

Gandhi once said, "A cow is a poem of compassion." Miss Emily is named after the poet Emily Dickinson. Emily Dickinson led a quiet life, so not many people knew how smart, sensitive, and talented she was. People have only recently begun to understand the intelligence and deep feelings that cows have. Miss Emily invites you to be *mooved* and inspired to explore your creativity through yoga, art, and writing!

Chair Yoga:
Lakshmi Voelker Chair Yoga, Yoga Certification Trainings, DVD-CD – http://getfitwhereyousit.com/.

Children's Yoga:
Angel Bear Yoga – A delightful and award-winning resource for Books, CDs, activities, teacher training, and much more, http://www.angelbearyoga.com/.

Radiant Child Yoga – Yoga-alliance certifications presented by Shakta Kaur Khalsa, author of Fly like a Butterfly: Yoga for Children (Portland, Or.: Rudra Press, 1998), and creator of The Radiant Child: Yoga In Motion DVD http://childrensyoga.com/.

Directories of Animal Sanctuaries:
United States – http://www.sanctuaries.org/

US and International: Farm Animal Sanctuary Guide – http://www.vegan.com/farm-sanctuaries/.

Information on Plant-based Diets:
Main Street Vegan – http://mainstreetvegan.net/.

Institute for Integrative Nutrition – http://www.integrativenutrition.com/.

Self-Expression and Therapeutic Writing:
International Academy for Poetry Therapy – http://www.technutworks.net/iapt/.

Fun Clothes & Gifts with Animal and Music Themes:
Beckhardt-Lada Design – https://www.facebook.com/beckhardtladadesign.

Animooves Products

Animooves Yoga Mat

**Animooves
Stainless Steel
Water Bottle**

**Animooves
Yellow T-Shirt**

**Miss Emily & Buttercup
Caribbean Blue T-Shirt**

**Binky for Animooves
Organic Natural T-Shirt**

To purchase these and many more items, check out our shop at cafepress.com/beckhardtladadesign, www.animooves.com, and look for the upcoming Animooves Companion Journal on Amazon.

Made in the USA
Middletown, DE
29 August 2015